Better Days

By: Anita "Nina" Porter

Better Days

DEDICATION

I want to thank God for giving me the ability to cross the finish line. Giving me the strength when I was in my weakest darkest moments. I thank him for giving me my babies Da'Najah Sa'Marah & Aa'Layah.

Da'Najah- You showed me that I can love a human forever, my first born you made the start of my life complete.

Sa'Marah –My twin second born you are the calm to my storm.

Aa'Layah- Baby Girl, the ending to my beautiful story you completed everything I asked for,

Better Days are coming.

Better Days

ACKNOWLEDGMENTS

4 years ago, I knew that I wanted to write my own book. I wanted to tell my story to inspire someone, I never cared about being judged about my story because it's MY STORY. I realized only God can judge me, so I started writing and couldn't stop.

Then I stepped back and realized I can put a twist onto my book, not only is my life mixed around in these chapters I added characters to Better Days.

In this process I want to thank Kylie Stores, you have no idea how much you encouraged me through my journey I'm forever thankful. Ja'Lisa Brown in just a short time you would not believe how much of a blessing you were to me. Lastly my family and friends for believing in me, staying patient. The wait is over…

Better Days

Better Days

Table of Contents

 Main Characters: Remi, Carla, Queene, Chewy, Jayshawn Da'Meire, Paul, & Robyn.

Better Days

Introduction

I just want to take the time to thank God for pushing me to follow my dream and write this book. This book will truly inspire someone in a good way. It's real, raw, and inspirational. I also want to thank my lovely girls Da'Najah and Sa'Marah & Aa'Layah because without them, I probably would still be talking about "BETTER DAYS" and not putting my book into action. Also, for the ones that made a difference in my life rather good or bad thank you! Please don't read in too deep but take notes and revaluate your life for the better. I want to make a difference in someone's life, and I hope I can.

To truly want something, you have to fight I struggled with so much I was motivated one day and distracted the next. I put my loyalty, blood, sweat, and tears is in this book, and I want to change a life not for just a person but for myself as well. I'm still rough around the edges, but my story is golden. I got chills writing this book because I didn't think that I had it in me. I always knew that I was smart and had a story to tell. My problem was I knew that there would be a judgmental person that would read my book and start judging me. IT'S OKAY because God keeps calling me to write it and I know that he is the only one that can judge me.

Before writing this book I always wanted to let everyone know that this was a calling. God always spoke to me on different occasions and told me to write this book I did not physically hear him, but he put so many people places and things in my life and it all lead to MY BOOK. I wanted to put my aunt in the introduction because herself and my mom was the first 2 people, I laid eyes on. She was there when my mom went in labor. I was there with her when she took her last breath. I remember me not seeing my aunt for a couple months and when I finally seen her, she was surprised. I had to tell her that I was trying to motivate myself to start my book and she proceeded to say, "Don't forget about me, I was there when you were born." I will never forget about you. Fly High Aunt Lonnie. After her passing, I learned to Pray, forgive, and let go. I also learned in life that things happen, and to never question it. Nothing! Death, relationship, problems, life, troubles, nothing because you will drive yourself crazy. Ask me how I know? I had so many deaths around me. I couldn't take people that mean the most to me pass away, but I had to pick myself back up. Life itself was very hard but when in doubt you have God by your side nothing negative matters, I'm telling you all this to say never give up!! I definitely used to sit back and overthink on why my life was such a mess. I felt like my whole world was at a standstill and I figured it out. I had to start removing toxic people, things, and situations out my life. I also had to stop praying to God for things that he knew weren't good for me. Until this very day he is working on my every move in life.

I ask him daily to shield me because some days are easier than others and some are hard to deal with. It's all on how much faith you have in God and in yourself. Another thing

I've noticed is, people love to see you down. Not all, but some. They live off the next person troubles, those are the ones you really have to look out for. Believe it or not, it can be your closest person in your life that's why you got to ask God to remove them. Sometimes your mind can play tricks on you it can have you thinking you need something, or have you believing something knowing that it's not. It can have you in a state of mind that you will think you're going crazy. Listen, your sanity is everything NEVER I mean never lose it and if you do, please get it under control before it controls you.

Coming back from losing your sanity is like being a baby all over again. You have to crawl before you start to regain strength, and sometimes in many cases your sanity was taking from another person actions. Life can really get you down it will chew you up and spit you out, but the question is can you overcome life? Life is a mystery you can be happy one day but then feel like your whole world is going to end I came to realize that in order for me to genuinely be happy even if I'm not! You can't let life always get to you because you will really think every time you wake up in the morning that something bad is going to happen. I say live a little and get comfortable with yourself because it's all a part of mental healing. You never know what a person is going through. I can honestly say that I been through so much. I mean being in a dark cave with no lights on having to crawl my way out a dark place, and I still am able to get up. The world can see the pain in your eyes, your posture, image everything changes and you yourself feel it in the inside.

Signs of depression and being stressed out can mess you up physically as well as not being in the right state of mind and overthinking. Being overwhelmed trying to overwork yourself can cause you to physically crash. My advice to anyone that can relate to anything I wrote is to take it one day at a time. Remember to live and learn from whatever you're going through. It will also be okay. God will lead the way just follow.

Better Days

Chapter 1

July 14th, 1988 (The Day a Queen was born) In this chapter the scene of the story is in the summertime July 14th, also it sets you the reader of the timeline of my REAL LIFE and some events that had taken place in my life.

Remi and Carla are best friends and have been for some time now. Remi and Carla did so much together. Their birthdays were four weeks and six days apart. Their families were very close. Remi's mother Robyn was a cook and her dad was in jail for robbery. Remi never knew much about her dad because her mother always held it down and shielded Remi. She had a stepfather named Paul, though that was there to raise her, although she wondered what it would feel like to be a daddy's girl, she actually was because Paul made her feel like she was his. Now Paul and Remi mother had three boys after Remi. One set of twins that were ten years of age, and the other brother was three years old and he was mentally challenged. It didn't matter their parents raised them to love Lil Paris just the way he was.

The unique thing about Lil Paris is he was very intelligent despite his disability. His speech wasn't very clear but everyone in Remi household knew exactly what he was saying and loved him no different. Remi was a little overprotective over Lil Paris and would let no one disrespect or make fun of him.

Now on the other hand Carla's life was a little shaky. Carla's mother was on drugs for years. Her mother wasn't the ordinary mother. She sold Carla and her sisters' clothes, shoes, food, and household items just to get high and Carla held a grudge against her for years because of it. Carla was raised by her father Curtis, he was always there, although Carla's parents were two different people. Curtis always loved Carla's mom Queene. Even though she was strung out on drugs you can still tell she was beautiful. She was dark skin, and Carla looked like her the most. Carla had an older sister and a younger sister. Carla oldest sister was 19 and was already out the house in college and Carla's younger sister Chewy was 6 years old and she looked up to Carla.

Everything Carla did Chew would follow. It really didn't matter what the two girls didn't have or went thru, they were so close to each other and never judged each other's situation. Often times Carla would sneak over to Remi's house because Queene would be so drunk, yelling and screaming playing loud music and drowning in her own misery. Carla would never be able to get sleep and she and Chewy didn't understand why their mother was so unhappy. Carla would write in her journal a lot and labeled it "Better Days" one her pages was so powerful that she reread it every day just to stay sane and it read:

Why?

Today has just been a little rocky for me. Why? I don't know I hate to see my mother strung out and hurt. I want her to be okay…she is a very beautiful person her struggles don't define her. I will pray for her and myself as well because this is not the person, I know she can be. It will get better one day. Or maybe NOT!!!

Carla was sure that she would take herself and her little sister away and out of the environment they had to endure. Carla just knew that better days were in the making. She had hope even if it had taken a little while. Both Remi and Carla were living in doubt about certain things that were going on in everyday life but always kept up with making sure they were okay and praying for Better Days.

Remi and Carla were sitting outside of the duplex home on 145th St where they always met up after doing their chores and getting dressed. It was the middle of summer, so it was hot, hazy, and there was so much to see at their view. They see cars riding by with loud music and boys walking by. Birds were chirping, weed & cigarette smell was in the air, the older boys were shooting dice and arguing about crapping out, and money was being owed to the winner of the game. The older ladies were sitting out catching the breeze and gossiping about the neighborhood speaking of the good old days. They were sipping lemonade and chuckling about how things were, but also concerned about how the way the world has become years later.

This particular day (July 14th) Remi and Carla wanted to explore the neighborhood just a little bit more. I mean they had already known about their neighborhood but had always been a little sheltered from their parents. So, they came up with a plan. Remi and Carla had the best idea, they were going to tell their parents that they were going to the park to play with some friends.

They knew that if they would have asked their parents, they would say no, only because of the way the neighborhood was set up, and how the way they were built is stature. Although they were 13, Remi didn't look it. She was 5'3 dark skin and very thick for her age. Remi's mother Robyn bought her clothes to hide her figure, but it didn't work. She was beautiful, had almond eyes, clear skin, purely white teeth, and had curly long hair that her mother always put into a ponytail. Carla was 5'1 and wasn't thick at all, she was very petite, but she wore belly shirts and small shorts because she wasn't form fitted. Carla was high yellow and had freckles. They were very attractive girls and their parents knew it. The girls came up with the park plan and their parents felt for it.

The next day Remi and Carla did their routine clean up and flew out the house halfway down the block. Carla little sister Chewy yelled "Carla daddy said take me with you." Carla was so mad but still eager to get out the house, so she followed behind happy as ever. As all three of the girls walked further into the neighborhood. They started to see things that they had NEVER seen before but couldn't turn back now. At one point of their adventure a black Impala had rode up on the side of the girls and rolled down the window to persuade Remi to come and talk to him. They all were startled and made a fast run to the park where they came across children and their parents that were able to help them if need be. Chewy was so happy to get with the other children at the park that she had forgot about the incident that had taken place, but Remi and Carla still thought about how they were getting home.

Remi was scared but knew that when the sun went down that it was time to head back home. In the meantime, the girls wanted to have fun as well, so they started playing with all the other kids at the park swinging on swings, monkey bars, running back and forth thru the water (Spray Park), and simply having the time of their life. Across from the spray park there was a basketball court full of all ages of boys playing a game of basketball. Carla and Remi tuned in so fast and was eager to walk over to watch the game. As they walked over both were a bit nervous entering the court it was half time, so the boys were on the side talking to the girls that were sitting on the bleachers. Remi and Carla were sitting talking amongst each other when two boys walked up to them and introduced their selves. One boy that said hello to Remi was very tall and had muscles and a very nice shape to be his age.

"Hey what's up shorty my name is Da'Meire, but everyone calls me Dae… what's your name?" He had a nice smile. Remi was instantly in shock. She couldn't talk. She was so attracted to how Da'Meire was so confident. She took a deep breath and answered, "Hi my name is Remi." Da'Meire was not shy he asked Remi "what took you so long to answer back?" Remi answered back with "Maybe I didn't want to give you my name." They both laughed. On the other end of the bench Carla and

Jayshawn kicked it off by just talking about sports because Carla was raised by her father and she was pretty familiar with Dwayne Wade and LeBron James. When Jayshawn started his conversation with Carla he went straight in with "Why you over here? You know nothing about what was going on out there on the court." Carla replied, "Yes I do you crossed over ole boy with the black gym shorts and you fouled him and hit a 3 pointer."

Jayshawn was amazed because he didn't know Carla knew. As the sun went down the girls forgot all about Chewy and knew they had to return home but came to realize that they didn't want to walk by their self so Carla asked Jayshawn can they walk them home. The boys agreed.

Jay was about 5'11 at the age of 16. He wasn't skinny at all he was physically fit with a nice box haircut and a very nice smile. He also had greenish brown eyes that lit up a room. As promised, they walked the girls home talking and getting acquainted. At the beginning of the girl's street they stopped the boys and told them that they were okay and that maybe they would see them next time. Remi said let's ask our parents if we can go to the park Friday to meet up.

That was the plan. They gave each other hugs and the boys said bye to Chewy. They went their separate ways. Before the girls went in the house, they grilled Chewy not to say a word about the day and gave her a dollar a piece and Chewy agreed. Carla and Remi said today as a good day.

Better Days

Better Days

Chapter 2

Growing Up (Let's get into how I grew up and how the character grew up as well.

By now the girls had met up with Jayshawn and Da'Meire plenty of times on several different occasions, and it's a safe to say that they are now boyfriend and girlfriends. Although they were in two different schools, they would meet up after school for an hour and just hang out going to the movies, skating, and just to socialize. Remi and Carla were just about due to graduate from middle school and enter into high school and the boys were sophomores in high school. They didn't care that the girls were younger than them. Jay and Dae actually had a reputation of being with younger girls, but Remi and Carla obviously didn't get the memo because of the school difference.

The boys even went out their way to attending the girl's 8th grade promotion and that's when they met the family. Remi introduce Da'Meire who happened to be standing in front of her mother. He had on a polo button down that was crispy and well ironed with some stone washed shorts and all white brand-new air forces. Dae wasn't afraid at all. He even reached out first and greeted them with a handshake. Remi was turned on by this and just knew Dae was so perfect for her. On the other hand, Carla introduced Jayshawn to her dad only because Carla was always ashamed of her mother even after being clean.

It always put a dark cloud over Carla because she never understood why her mother did the things she did. Carla always remembered when her mother was in rehab and her father had taken her down there to see Queene and she denied the visit. A couple days later a letter came in the mail and Carla was in rage but deep down inside she wanted to hear with Queene had to say so she opened it, and, on the paper, Carla read:

Carla,

Hello baby, how are you? I am very sick and didn't want to see you and Chewy. You girls are too young to understand. Your older sister Christina already doesn't want anything to do with me and I understand that I messed up, but I am trying to get better. I promise to be a better mother that I should be for you and your sisters. Please understand. Lastly, always listen to your father because he is the best thing that happened to you girls. I am forever grateful! I love you and see you soon.

Even with that letter Carla heart was black, when it came to her mother Queene, but her father didn't play the disrespect to their mother, so Carla just kept everything stored inside.

Queene sat alone as the girls introduced Jay and Dae, but Chewy had other plans. She loved her mother, so she grabbed Jay by his hand and yelled "Mommy this is Carla's boyfriend Jayshawn." Chewy was so excited she looked at Jay and said "say hi to my mom boy" LOL. Jay smiled and said, "Hello Ms. Queene nice to finally meet you". Carla's mom was delighted and responded with "how are you young man?" The conversation was good and after the promotion Remi and Carla came up with a plan.

The girls wanted to have one on one time with Jay and Da'Meire so they asked their parents if they can go to the movies with there now boyfriends. Remi's mother was hesitating and so was Carla's father. Queene was fine with it but everybody didn't agree so that plan was shut down, but Carla and Remi had cell phones, so they talked to their boyfriends for hours after they went home. They talked about everything from school, sports, parents, and most of all sex. The girls knew what sex was. Remi's mother talked to Remi and Carla about sex. She always told the girls that sex could wait and if that was all the boys wanted then they really don't care. They were taught to be patient, but the girls had another thing in mind. They felt like they were ready to take it to the next level with Jay and Dae. The girls thought that because they were going into high school that it was most definitely time to lose their virginity to their boyfriends. Carla and Remi were anxious, excited, and scared, but adventurous at the same time. This was all a part of growing up and the girls were going to eventually find out.

Chapter 3

HAZELWOOD (The Jungle) is in the heart of Pittsburgh. A neighborhood that was well known. This is where I spent my life at. Hazelwood was the Jungle it taught me so many things and open my eyes to a lot, in this chapter it really talks about my childhood but in the setting of the characters.

Throughout the summer there was a lot of sitting on laps, grinding, and kissing. The four of them were at the park late night and Carla thought that it was the right time. She whispered into Jayshawn's ear and told him to follow her over to the slide. The lights were getting dim so Remi and Da'Meire couldn't really see what was about to go down. Jay started kissing Carla and Carla kissed back Carla knew that he was experienced because of the way he was kissing her. He stuck his tongue into her mouth and she instantly followed. Her heart was beating so fast, but she knew that she couldn't back out now. Carla and Remi always talk about when it happened it should be special with the right person. Carla felt in her heart that Jayshawn was definitely the one. Carla started to get the hang of what Jay was doing she started to give him wet kisses on his neck. Jay followed by lifting Carla skirt up and pulling down her underwear. The night was getting darker and they didn't care were Remi and Dae were.

Jay immediately started giving Carla small kisses on her stomach and between her thighs. Carla didn't know how to feel. She was excited, curious, and scared all at the same time. Carla knew what Jay was about to do, and that's what he did. Carla couldn't believe how experienced he was. She knew this wasn't his first time. As she laid there, she couldn't help but to moan he went faster causing her legs to shake. After he got done, he asked Carla was she okay. Carla couldn't even speak. She just shook her head yes then he asked her was she ready? She then spoke and said "yes" Jay entered Carla slowly because he knew she was a virgin. She moaned and grabbed onto him in a panic as he stroked her. He looked at her and asked was she okay? She replied yes and for about ten minutes he stroked in and out. When he seen that Carla was comfortable, he went faster until he ejaculated. Jay held on to Carla and kissed her softly. After they were done, they put their clothes on and walked back over to Remi and Dae like nothing never happened Carla legs felt like noodles and she felt like she just wanted to shower.

The look Remi gave her was in disappointment. She was also anxious to know what happened. It was now late, and Carla had made up a lie to her mom so that she could stay over Remi's house. It all came out. Carla was excited to tell Remi how it went, and Remi was excited as well. Remi asked so many questions "Did it hurt?" "Girl do you think he liked it?" "In the park though?" You nasty! Carla answered every question with confidence.

After taking a shower, Carla called her boyfriend and talked to him while Remi and Dae were on the phone until they fell asleep. As Carla slept, she dreamed of what happened and just knew she was in love. She thought about how Jay knew how to do all of those sexual things to her while being so young, but she was on cloud 9 until things took a turn for the worst.

Better Days

Chapter 4

Allderdice (A Pittsburgh Public School that I attended and graduated from. Also, now in the book the girls Remi and Carla are now in High School and is now going thru real-life situations as I did when I was in high school.)

Although Carla gave up her virginity to Jayshawn that summer, the girls were going into high school. Remi and Dae didn't do anything but kiss. Remi was ready but wanted it to be special Da'Meire wasn't trying to hear that though. They often had arguments about Remi waiting because Carla gave it up. They had several talks about Carla and Jay. The boys were going into the 11th grade and the girls were only freshman and also new to the school. Carla and Remi talked their parents into letting them go to the same school as the boys and after a thousand NO's they finally said yes. The girls were so excited especially Carla. She wanted to be around Jay at all times, but Jay had another agenda. He was already known for being the ladies' man but knew he had to play it cool because he didn't want Carla to go off. A week before school the girls went school shopping. They both wanted to have so much.

Remi's Cousin Janelle also went to Allderdice High School but was in the 10th grade and was known for shop lifting. She often got the girls clothes here and there but thought it was time for them to jump off the porch and talk them into getting their own clothes. That particular day was the scariest day of Carla and Remi's life even though Janelle talked them down to what to do and not do they were shaking. The crazy thing was the girl's parents gave them money to go shopping but Janelle laughed at how much they had and said, "Wow that's all and chuckled". What are you going to get with that? We are in high school you need more stop being scared. DAMN."

She kept talking to the girls. The whole bus ride was BLAH BLAH BLAHHHH. Then Remi finally told her cousin to "SHUT UP BITCH DAMN" we already scared "WTF." The bus ride went fast and before you knew it all three girls were getting off the bus with several other girls from the neighborhood kids of all ages going school shopping. As they entered the mall Janelle was excited and lit up like a Christmas tree. She had that glow in her eyes because she was good at what she did. She was so good that she had already called a personal ride that was already outside waiting for her and the girls so they wouldn't have to wait for the bus. If their bags got too full, they would be able to go dump clothes out and go back in. The first store was Victoria Secret. The girls entered the store and the employee greeted them. All the girls spoke. Janelle was so sneaky she went to work shoving clothes into her purse and still trying to encourage the girls to get to work. She whispered, "Come on bitches what the fuck are yall waiting for?" Carla and Remi gave each other looks and started filling their bags up as well.

Before the big exit Remi came up with a plan. She didn't care what her cousin said she picked up a shirt and purchased it as Carla and Janelle walked out the store. Once she was done, she walked out the store like nothing happened and Carla did the same routine. They took turns until the girls hit every store. Janelle didn't participate in buying anything. She was cocky with what she did. A couple hours had gone by and after dumping clothes into Janelle's personal car, it was time to go. The girls gathered all their clothes and Janelle was still talking. "See bitches I told you it was going to work, you just have to be careful," "Get it how live even though you was buying shit." Nelle started laughing and said, "all scary." Remi cut her off and said "Oh the fuck well shit we was scared. That was a distraction" and rolled her eyes at Nelle.

When they got close to their neighborhood the girls went to Remi house. Her mom was at work. As they laid their clothes out, Remi Car

& Nelle were happy. They didn't
even care how and what they had to
do to get it. The end of the summer
went fast and before you knew it the
first day of school arrived. Remi and
Carla were swaged out from head
to toe. Janelle also knew how to do
hair, so she hooked everyone up.
Walking to the bus stop Carla
looked like a million bucks. She
wore a pink outfit and a pair of all
white huaraches with her book bag
and boxed braids that Nelle did.
She had little baby hairs down
because Nelle had plaited her hair
to perfection. Carla also wore
bamboo earrings and Alex and
Annie bangles. Her lips were
glossy, and she smelt delicious.
Remi slayed it as well. She wore a
pair of jeans that had been cut up
from Hollister and had a Hollister
shirt that matched with a pair of
Chuck Taylors. Remi couldn't take
the pain of Nelle braiding her hair,

so she got her cousin to slick her hair back to a ponytail with a swoop. She rocked stud earrings, her lip gloss popping, her book bag matched her outfit, and she smelled good as well. They were ready.

As the bus arrived the girls hopped on and they were anxious and ready for their big day. Not to mention to see their boyfriends. Allderdice was filled with blacks, whites, Jewish any nationality you could think of. Carla and Remi didn't have any classes together but gym and that was 6th period. They also had the same lunch. The girls finally met up with Jay and Dae with a group of other people including girls. Jayshawn was being flirtatious with one of the girls in the crowd until Carla walked up to him and said "hello Jayshawn" in a voice that quickly aggravated him. He replied back with "What's up Carla?" with a look to die for. The girls walked away from Jay. Remi and Dae had gone in to eat lunch. Carla yelled at Jay and said "what the fuck was that Jay? You playing me now?" Jay smiled and said "baby it's not like that, but every female you see me with you cannot spaz the fuck out. Chill the fuck out." He looked at her and wrapped his arms around her. He whispered in her ear "Can I get some after school?" She looked behind him and forgot about what happened and said, "yes boo." The day went by so quick and Carla was over Jay's mother's house having sex with him like they normally did because Jay's mother was never home. She felt so loved by him but knew that something was up and didn't want her feelings hurt. She was in love. She knew that better days were near, or were they? That was a question that always set in the back of Carla's mind

Better Days

Better Days

Chapter 5

Da'Najah (Strong Determined and Stubborn) I went thru a lot of what I wrote about in this chapter and soon after at a young age I conceived my first daughter and named her Da'Najah. It was so much chaos going on in my life at that time of me being pregnant with her and then there was life. A beautiful one, so in this chapter it starts to get chaotic for the characters and life truly begins for not only myself in real life but for Remi and Carla.

As the months went by, the same things happened. Carla would catch Jay doing things in school. She found numbers in his phone and she had enough. On this day particular, she went over to his mother's house and knocked on the door. She knew that he was home she banged and banged until Jays mother Mrs. La' Shawn came to the door. "Hi Carla, how are you?" Carla responded, "I'm fine, can I speak with Jayshawn please?" His mother said "sure." As Carla walked up the steps to Jayshawn's room she felt weak when she got to the top of the staircase. Jay's door was closed with his music up loud. Carla opened the door and their Jay was having sex with the girl she had seen him with the first day of school. Carla was furious and dove on Jayshawn yelling, fighting, and screaming trying to beat the girl's ass. Carla didn't care who was naked, she was ready to beat both of them down. After he instructed the girl to get dressed and leave while, he held Carla down. She became angrier. "Fuck you Jayshawn you aren't shit I hate you swear." Jay yelled back "I can explain Carla." She didn't want to hear it. "Fuck you I'm done!" She screamed. "You been disrespecting me for a long time, and this is where I draw the fucking line." She punched him in his face. Jayshawn knew to never hit a girl but he went against everything his mother had taught him and punched Carla back. She collapsed and fell to the floor. His mother ran up the steps to see what all the commotion was about. When she reached her sons room, she seen Carla on the floor crying with a big knot on her head from Jay hitting her. Carla knew that this couldn't be life she ran out the house and headed to Remi house.

When she arrived, Remi screamed "what the fuck happened?" As she got ice for Carla, she explained what happened and told Remi she would never go back with Jayshawn again. Weeks went by with no calls from Jay or Carla to each other. They even stopped speaking in school. Jay wanted to talk to Carla, but she avoided him. She was simply done with Jayshawn.

But on a good note Dae and Remi wasn't trying not to get into Carla and Jayshawn mess. With all of Carla and Jay's madness and issues, Da'Meire had asked Remi out on a date to the movies to watch the Black Panther and Remi agreed. She was tired of hearing what happened with Jay and Carla and wanted to be with her man, so Remi called to see what time the movie started, and they enjoyed their date. After the movie Dae had asked Remi if she wanted to go to his house to eat dinner. Remi called her mother and ask if she could stay out a little longer. Her mother asked

Remi would she be with Da'Meire. Remi answered with "yes ma, I'll be home shortly don't worry." When they arrived at Da'Meire's house nobody was home. The house was dark and quiet. Dae turned on all the lights and heated up some food. They sat and talked about Black Panther and laughed the night away until Remi realized what time it was. Dae insisted that she stay. Remi had a plan. She called Nelle up and started the conversation:

 What bitch what you want? Remi replied...

 Damn is that the way to answer your phone?

 What? Janelle knew Remi was up to something.

Can you call my mom and tell her that I missed my bus and that the only place I could go to was your house? Tell her I got so tired that I

57

fell asleep at your house, and that you only called because my phone was dead.

You get on my nerves but, yes, I will, and you owe me.

 I know cousin I got you call me back to tell me what she said

 Okay bye.

Ten minutes later Nelle gave Remi the okay that her mom was good, and she was calling in the morning to see if they made it school the next day. Remi said, "okay thanks cousin I'll see you bright and early tomorrow."

Remi and Dae watched movies for about an hour and then it happened. Remi started dozing off and Da'Meire kissed on her softly. She opened her eyes and kissed him back. They undressed each other and Da'Meire started sucking

on Remi nipples. Although Remi
was a virgin, she watched plenty of
pornos. Dae laid her down and
kissed her stomach and then
started performing oral sex. He hit
all the right spots. Remi moaned
loud and louder and got scared of
why she was feeling the way she
felt. Da'Meire whispered to her and
said its okay baby you bust your
first nut.

As he made his way back up
to her to take Remi's virginity her
legs were still shaking from him
giving her head, but she always
replayed with her mother and Carla
told her: "NO GLOVE NO LOVE."
She asked Da'Meire did he have
one and surprisingly he did. He put
it on and took it slow. He entered
into Remi and felt her juices. She
moaned and moaned as they made
love. In the middle of them making
love Da'Meire's condom broke he

leaned back and took it off. Remi was on cloud 9 that she didn't even notice it. Towards the end Da'Meire had ejaculated but he did not pull out. The moment was hot and heated. After they were done, the two of them laid there and fell asleep. While Dae held Remi, she dreamed that this would last forever, but she had knew what her friend had went through, so she held her guard up.

The next few months Carla and Jayshawn really didn't talk at all. Jay tried to reach out and relay messages thru Remi and Dae, but it didn't get far. Although Carla's childhood wasn't perfect her father raised her. He always told her that a real man should never beat on a woman. Carla was still in love with Jay but knew that he wouldn't change so she met a boy in school named James. It was nothing much just hanging out movies, homework, talking etc. James had already known about Jayshawn but liked Carla so much he didn't care. James was on the wrestling team and was physically fit. Carla thought to herself this is Déjà vu with dating a guy in sports but that's all she was attracted too. James was everything Carla imagined. Even without sex it was just magical. It had only been a month and Carla bragged about James while Remi listened. Remi had not been feeling too good lately. She stopped Carla from talking and said Hey C I feel sick. Carla asked Remi how long she has been feeling sick. Remi responded, "maybe a few weeks I'm going to ask my mom to make an appointment." Carla just thought Remi was coming down with a cold, so she didn't press the issue. Remi laid in bed and slept as Carla talked to James for hours. What woke

Remi up was the sound of her cell phone. It was Dae:

Hello Boo! (Sounding Sleepy)

What's up Rem Boo you okay you sound sleep?

Yes, I was Boo I haven't been feeling good.

What's wrong what's hurting you?

My stomach and body is aching and I'm always tired I'm going to get my mom to make me an appointment soon.

Okay well get some rest. I wanted you to come over so that we can cuddle together.

Not tonight boo I'll talk to you tomorrow in school.

Remi slept the night away and woke up at six in the morning vomiting. She felt it in her sleep, Remi's mom had heard all the noises and woke up. She walked to the bathroom and asked Remi was she okay. Remi was so sick she couldn't stand on her two feet. She was weak and didn't know why. Remi finally said mommy I need to go to the hospital; I don't feel too good. Remi's mother agreed she seen how her daughter body looked so instead of going to school her and her mother went into the emergency room. Remi was cold so she wore sweatpants, a shirt, and tennis shoes with her hair in a messy bun. The two arrived at the hospital and was seen fast. The Dr. asked several questions:

Good morning Remi…

I'm going to ask you several questions is it okay if your mother sits in?

It's okay Remi replied

I see that you have been feeling weak sleeping and vomiting? Can we run a couple tests to rule things out?

Yes, you can

Are you sexually active?

Remi's eyes got so big and she got even colder. She had not told her mother that she and Da'Meire have been having sex. So, the only thing to do was lie for some reason.

No, I'm still a virgin.

Okay well when was your last menstrual cycle?

Ummmmm a few months ago. I figured it was late and didn't pay it any attention.

Remi mother looked at the Dr. then Remi.

Can you give me a urine sample?

Remi agreed. The Doctor walked out the room and let Remi give a urine sample. Dr. Smith's nurse came in to collect Remi urine sample. As they waited for the doctor, Remi's mother told her that she hopes that he finds out what's wrong with her and went to hug her. 20 minutes went by and the doctor came in with a worried look on his face.

Remi you mentioned earlier that you weren't sexually active RIGHT?

Yes! She was getting annoyed.

Well you are well over two months pregnant.

Remi mother: "What THE FUCK? OH, HELL NO THIS MUST BE A MIX UP REMI IS NOT EVEN HAVING SEX."

Remi is two months and three weeks she will be three months next week.

Remi mom: "ARE YOU KIDDING ME?"

Remi started crying mom. "I'm sorry I was going to tell you that me and Da'Meire" ---- Remi's mother stopped her and yelled "YOU AND DA'MEIRE WHAT THE FUCK." I CAN'T BE A GRANDMOTHER YOU ARE TOO YOUNG REMI." Remi's mom starting crying in the hospital room. She was hurt and angry. Remi sat there crying as well. The doctor left the two alone and Remi's mother started the conversation. "Remi what are you going to do with a baby huh? You're in the 9th grade. You are way too young to have a damn baby you're a baby yourself." "And when were you going to tell me you were having sex?" Remi started crying even harder. Robyn yelled at Remi to stop crying. "We are going to talk to your stepfather and Da'Meire parents." We are going to get to the bottom of this. "LET'S GO REMI!" Robyn yelled as she stormed out the hospital doors. She entered the car. She was hurt trying to collect her thoughts and get it together. Robyn finally calmed down halfway home and asked Remi a couple questions.

Remi why didn't you tell me you were having sex?

Mommy I was afraid (Remi started crying again) Mommy Dae and I used protection. I don't know what happened. You always told me to make sure I protected myself.

Well something happened you are almost three months pregnant. I feel kind of responsible because I wasn't on top of your period cycle how I usually am. We need to get things together because things could get better or worse for you. Let's figure things out.

Mommy I'm so sorry. Please forgive me I never meant for this to happen.

The drive home after that was complete silence. Remi texted Dae a crying emoji. He replied back "What's wrong?"

Remi texted back "We need to talk after school, please come over to my house." "Okay" he replied.

Remi paced her floor in her room listening to Robyn and Paul her stepdad talk. She was in total shock. She hadn't even told Carla she and Dae had sex let alone that she was pregnant, so she decided to text her at lunch time. Remi texted Carla and said:

So, a couple months ago Dae and I had sex.

A couple minutes later Carla texted back WHAAAAAAT Bitch and you weren't going to tell me WYA?

Remi replied: I'm at home but there is more I'm almost three months pregnant. As soon as Remi hit the send button Carla called her. "Remi picked up and Carla started screaming BITCH HUH?" "What the fuck are you talking about?" Remi explained that Dae put a condom on and she wasn't sure if he had taken it off or if it broke. Carla listened. She knew this was serious and had to be by her best friend's side so she told Remi she would be over later on. Things were about to get very deep for Remi and Dae very deep.

Better Days

Chapter 6

Sa'Marah (Brings love and a new start to life). In my life I had to face so many silent battles, in this particular chapter so did the characters. Sa'Marah is my 2nd daughter and she had brought me love and a new fresh start of my hurt and pain that I had experienced at an early age. Also, in this chapter Remi went thru a life changing experience as well.

Two months had gone by and Remi and Dae's parents had sat down several times to talk it over. They all came to an agreement that Remi and Dae were too young to be parents, but she was too far along to abort the baby. They had no choice to help and support kids having a baby, but nothing was going to change. Remi and Dae were going to continue on going to school, graduate, and stay in sports. They were going to find jobs and attend all of Remi appointments. This was so hard on Remi and Dae but they both knew it wouldn't be easy. One day Remi and Dae were talking and Remi was just curious. She said "well did you take the condom off? Or did it break?" Dae responded "it broke boo but we were in the moment and I didn't want to mess anything up." Remi felt a little trapped because she had listened to her mother and still ended up pregnant.

She was confused, hurt, mislead, and knew that her life was really going to change. Carla and Remi really didn't hang out as much because Remi was pregnant. She really couldn't do much, so Carla had met a couple girls from school. She was well over Jayshawn and she and James were serious now.

All her friends she hung around with now were gorgeous, fly, stacked had nice bodies banging, were swaged out, and loved to have fun. They did almost everything together. The ringleader was Tionna. She was in the 11th grade. She was very bold in looks. All the colors she wore even down to the jewelry, she went big. Tionna was light brown skin and had freckles on her face but her confidence was to the roof. Then there was Evelyn, but everyone called her Eve. Now Eve was more of the firecracker although she was pretty, she was a fighter and didn't take no shit. Her swag was Jordan's and Pink outfits. She was never really girly because she always wanted to be ready. She had a dark coffee complexion and always had nice and neat braids in cornrows. She was super cute. All three girls were the talk of the school.

James friends were having a party at a hall and everybody that knew James was invited. The girls were ready. They couldn't wait to put their outfits together and get their hair and nails done. Tionna's sister was 21 and agreed to get the girls a bottle of Hennessey. Everything was put into play before Saturday. Carla went by Remi's house to check on her because she had called and got no answer. Remi and Carla were still best friends but there were a lot of things Remi couldn't do anymore because she was now five months going on six months.

Carla knocked on the door and it took Remi a little while to answer. When she answered she turned back around to walk back in the house. Carla sensed her attitude and said "Hi Bitch, damn you weren't going to answer your phone. What's that about? I brought you some snacks fatty for my niece or nephew" Remi replied, "Girl I'm just going thru it who would of ever thought I would be pregnant my freshman year I'm jealous!" Dae still gets to go out and party, go to practice while I'm sitting here getting fat and shit." Carla went to go rub Remi's stomach she said, "sis this won't be forever". "You got this." Remi asked Carla was she still coming to find out the gender of the baby. Carla yelled, "Yeah I wouldn't miss it for nothing in the world." Remi looked and felt a little better but wanted to be petty, so she said to Carla "oh I only asked that because you got two new bitches that you been around. Let me find out their taking my place. Bitches might catch a beat down. Remi uttered! "Can't nobody take my place" Carla laughed and headed to the door and before she left, she said "Sissy I love you and nobody will ever take your place. I got to go and get ready for James party you know it's coming up a bitch needs to get dolled up and cute." "I know" Remi answered back. "Dae was going to go but decided not to. He's going to come over and keep me company, plus he doesn't want Jayshawn to feel no type of way." Carla looked in disgust. She had not talked to her first love ever since that day he put his hands on her. She dreamed about getting back with him, but knew she was better than that whole situation. She often seen him at school and walked past him. He still was the same; a straight hoe the same as when he was with Carla. She wasn't missing nothing. "Well bye sissy I got to go I love you so much and she went down to kiss Remi's stomach and started talking to her unborn niece or nephew." She said, "auntie baby, I love you I can't wait to meet you." Carla always felt good when she talked to Remi. She was truly her best friend.

The days seemed like they were going fast. Saturday was here and it was time to party. Carla, Tionna, and Eve were on go. They all met up at Eve's house because it was the closest to the hall. Before they all met up, James called Carla. She had already known what James wanted so Carla went over. As soon as she entered James room, they immediately started drinking. Carla could smell the liquor on James breath but for some reason she liked when James was a little intoxicated. He was focused and kissed every part of her body. He ate her like he was starving. She couldn't control herself her moans got louder and louder! When he was done, she knew she had to return the favor, so she went down on him. Although Carla was younger, she somewhat knew what she was doing. She always imagined sucking a Popsicle. Ten minutes into sucking his penis he was ready to have sex. He bent Carla over and went deep inside of her. Carla was on cloud 9. She moaned away and took every stroke until James had ejaculated. They both were stuck afterwards for about an hour. Carla looked at her phone and jumped up and told James "Boo we have a party to get ready for." James replied with "I know, but I had to taste my baby before, or I wouldn't have had a good night." Carla smiled "well I'm about to shower before your mom gets back then I'm going to head over Eves house, and I'll see you later."

Carla got to Eve's house fast and they were already drinking, and smoking weed. Eve's grandma was at BINGO. That's who Eve lived with, so the girls decided to get dressed there. The weed was definitely in the air, perfume was being sprayed, and Hennessey was getting poured. The girl's slayed that night. All three of them looked bomb. The girls were ready for James party. It was only a couple blocks away, and they just decided to walk, drink, smoke, and talk. Tionna started the conversation off with "Girl where the fuck was you at? She said to Carla.

Carla: Damn bitch you're nosey.

Eve: Started laughing "Girl; you was at James house Huh?

Carla: Why? Bitches is NEBBY.
Carla, started to laugh with the girls.
Well since you must know yes, I
was over James house. I had to
give my boo a little boost and she
laughed. Tionna and Eve looked at
each other and started laughing and
both said together "NASTY"
laughing louder.

Although Tionna and Eve
were having sex too they were a
little older than Carla. They talked
more until they were at the hall.
Soon as they arrived, they heard
loud music and people walking up
to the building. When the girls
entered the party, it was cracking.
Carla knew James was popular, but
it was lit and that's everything
James had bragged about for a
whole week. Carla instantly started
dancing! Tionna followed. They
couldn't stop. Eve 2-stepped back
and forth. She really wasn't a

dancer, but she started opening up. After an hour, Carla started to look for James. It was packed.

There was booty shaking, the smell of sweat, and different types of colognes and perfumes filled the air. Carla's ears were popping. The DJ was definitely on his ones and twos. When Carla found James, he was dancing with a chick that Carla had seen around in school and Carla instantly got an attitude. She walked over to James and yelled "HELLO!" James was drunk and didn't even notice Carla, but he stopped dancing once Carla got in between the two of them. Instead of whooping her ass, she made her mad and took her man back by grinding all over him. James wrapped his arms around the back of her and whispered in Carla's ear "YOU'RE A MESS." Carla replied with "What I do? I could have beat her ass but no I just took what was mines." They both started laughing the DJ got on the mic and said, "Let's see the ladies shake some ass."

The DJ screamed over his mic. As soon as he said that all you seen and heard was the girls screaming in excitement and grabbing a dude. BLAC YOUNGSTAs hit Booty came on and there was ass shaking in the whole party. Carla even looked over at Eve and she was twerking. It was lit. Carla grinded all over James bouncing and dropping. She was in the moment and James enjoyed every minute of it. He grabbed Carla's waist and pictured them having sex earlier and start pumping on Carla. He whispered to Carla again "You're staying over my house tonight." Carla knew she couldn't but texted her dad and asked can she stay over Eves house. Minutes later she got the text that it was okay. She told her dad she loved him, and they were ready to go.

Another text came thru the phone from her dad. He wrote:

Hey C, have Eves grandma call me I need to confirm if she's okay with you staying.

Carla instantly got an attitude and was annoyed and let James read the message. There was no way Carla was going to have Eves grandma vouch for her. So, Carla knew the idea of staying the night with James was over.

Carla enjoyed the rest of the night with James and was a little tipsy and high. She loved the feeling. Her night had just begun, but she respected her dad so after the party they all walked home together laughing, singing, smoking, and enjoying the rest of the night. Eve got dropped off first because her house was the closest. Next was Tionna and one of James friends Andre that had been trying to get on Tionna walked her to the door. While he was doing that James was all cuddled up kissing and grinding on Carla getting his feels on while Andre and Tionna talked a little more outside her house. James had felt so good with Carla he blurted out "I'm so glad that nigga fucked up because now I got you." Carla giggled and said, "yeah okay I'm yours", but don't let me see no bitches on you or I'm going nuts LOL. That shit wasn't cute, and she wasn't cute all crusty and busted don't play with me boo!" Carla looked at James. He said, "it won't happen again." Then minutes later Andre walked back over with the biggest smile on his face from

Tionna giving him her number. They continued on walking Carla home. After a couple blocks of talking and ripping, they reached Carla house. She wanted to stay with James so bad but didn't know how she would get by her father. But it was cool she had fun and James had promised to call her as soon as he got home. They both were faded. Carla got in the house where her family was watching a movie.

Chewy: Hey Carla, did you have fun at you boyfriend's party?

Carla: Yes, I did dang little girl.

Queene: Hey baby.

Carla: Hey mom.

Carla didn't really want to speak. She loved her mom but still had anger in her heart for her and Queene felt it. Carla's dad was surprised to see her. "Carla, I thought you were staying over Eve house what happened?" Carla started walking up the steps. She began "Oh daddy never mind she had something to do for her grandma in the morning and I just wanted to sleep in."

Carla's dad didn't press the issue and said okay. Carla had gone into her room and texted James and Remi. She knew Remi would probably be sleep, but James texted back instead of them talking on the phone. The two just texted all night until Carla couldn't text. She was sleep like a baby.

Weeks had gone by and it was time for Remi to find out what the gender of her and Da'Meire baby was. At this point everyone was happy and excited. Only two people could go into the room with Remi and of course Dae went in. Remi's mom went back as well while everyone else waiting in the waiting room. Remi was nervous but at this point she didn't care what the gender was she just wanted her baby to be healthy. As they entered the room Remi was amazed, she never had done this. The doctor instructed Remi to get onto the bed and relax.

She then asked Remi to pull up her shirt and that she would put warm gel on her stomach, the Doctor was very experienced from what Remi mother could see. Remi took a deep breath and looked at Da'Meire. She couldn't believe that there was a baby inside of her stomach. Remi started to cry. She knew that she was too young to have a baby, but when she seen the baby on the monitor it was real. The doctor took a couple of pictures of Remi and Dae's baby and after 15 minutes the doctor asked, "are you ready for me to reveal what the sex of your baby is?" Remi's mother started to cry too. They both held Remi hands the doctor said Remi you are having a girl. Remi couldn't believe she knew what was growing inside of her. She was so emotional she wanted to go out to the waiting room and let everyone know what she was having. Da'Meire was happy as well. The Doctor finished up the exam and told Remi and Dae that their baby girl was growing perfect. She ended it with pictures for them to take with them. Remi and Dae revealed to their family that IT WAS A GIRL, and everyone jumped for joy. Remi's mother also announced that nothing would change. She wanted Remi and Dae to finish school and for Remi to go all the way until she goes into labor. Dae's mother agreed they both will go to school. Carla hugged Remi so tight and told her she promised

Remi she would help her raise her "niece pooh". She often talked to Remi stomach and now that she knew what she was having, Carla always said her or niece pooh. Remi needed to figure out a name. She wanted to name her after Dae and herself and after months of going back and forth she named her Da'Marie Remi.

On the day she was born, her labor was not what she expected. She went two weeks over her due date, and she was miserable. After 23 hours of labor she had to get a C-Section that scared her and put her in a panic. Remi cried and didn't know what was going on and what to do. She had been pushing for so long with no signs of baby Da'Marie. Remi was so exhausted that she had given up. Dae was in total shock this was his first time ever experiencing labor. Remi's mother had to coach Dae and Remi. Remi cried in pain she was over it she was young and didn't know that labor would feel like she was dying. Carla came into the room and calmed Remi down. Remi was so glad to see Carla she felt at ease for some reason Remi asked for Dae and Carla to stay in the room while she had to get the C-Section. Remi and Da'Meire's mother felt some type of way but anything to keep her calm and ready to welcome Da'Marie into the world. So, they agreed to sit in the next room on standby. Carla looked at Remi and said okay bitch let's get my niece pooh out. Dae was still out of it even after he heard that Remi's birth canal was too small. Everything was happening so fast with the 2 teenagers. After Carla calmed Remi down, the doctor came into the room to go over the procedure that was about to take place. They placed a long needle into Remi's spinal area... and told her that she would go numb from her waist on down, and it kicked in quick! Remi started to get scared because she never felt this feeling before, but Carla was there by her side. As she laid there once the procedure started, they placed a white sheet over Remi stomach to shield her from seeing the procedure. She looked over to Carla and asked her was everything okay. Carla said, "yes relax sis you got this." The doctor went to work. They cut Remi's bikini line and started to pull her baby out. After ten minutes, the doctor gave Dae some scissors to cut the umbilical cord, and he went back over to Remi. They didn't hear a cry yet until they suctioned her mouth and she had a set of lungs on her. Carla cried when she heard her niece for the first time. The doctor weighed her, and she came out 8lbs and 9oz. The doctor wrapped her up and laid her on Remi chest. Remi couldn't believe her eyes she fell in love. She was so beautiful and looked just like Da'Meire.

Dae went to hold his daughter and fell in love. He couldn't stop looking at her. He promised her that he would always be there for her and that he would be her first love. Now it was time for Carla to hold Da'Marie. She still was teary eyed. The birth of Da'Marie Remi was beautiful. After the procedure was over the doctors worked on Remi, she and the baby had transferred her into their own room. Family and friends poured into the room to welcome Baby Da'Marie Remi, she was beautiful, Remi was exhausted and after hours of company she just wanted to rest. As everyone left, she slept after the nurse came into take the newborn and place her in the nursery. She dreamed of what just had taken place, and she didn't know how to be a mother. She was afraid but knew that she would try her hardest to be the best mother she can be and prayed that there were better days to come.

Better Days

Chapter 7

Life- I never knew how my life would turn out, with not growing up without my biological father. Not going to a major college with making bad decisions that would reflect on my future, but I never gave up. I always went with the flow of things, but I too was a worrier. I felt like every second, minute, hour, month, and year counted. So, I had to make the best out it. In this chapter so did the characters, decisions were made, LIFE just happened and there was nothing I can do nor the characters.

Some people take life for granted. They play with it like the human body has nine lives. Once you're gone your gone. There are many chances that you can get in one life.

The birth of Da'Marie made Carla look at life different she knew that she had to make it right with her mother Queene. Carla's mother had been clean for some years now, and it was a burden on her heart that she doesn't open up to her mother. Months had gone by and Carla just didn't know how to cope with things so she would drink, smoke, and write in her diary. On this particular day her heart was heavy, so she wrote:

Dear Diary,

Just one of those days, I want to talk to my mom to tell her how much I love her, but I'm still angry! The shit isn't fair that my sisters and I had to go thru that because she wanted to do drugs. My dad struggled with raising us while she was in and out of rehabilitation centers. Man, fuck this I'm out. I will never be able to talk to her.

The next day she wrote:

Dear Diary,

Feeling a little better. Every day I get stronger and better. One day my mom and I will have that bond. Please God help me forgive. I'm giving it up to you. God you are really the only one that can heal my broken heart. I love my mom, but I can't forgive I just need guidance.

The day after Carla wrote in her diary, Carla's father had come to talk to her in the living room. "Hey C what you doing?" "Nothing dad." Carla replied back. "I have to talk to you about your mom. She wanted to tell you, but you are so distant from her you all barely speak, and she doesn't want to intervene, but this must stop." Carla tried to cut him off "But Daddy!" "CARLA!" her dad yelled. "Your mother is sick okay!! She has breast cancer!" Her Father started tearing up. Carla didn't know what to say. She felt like a car had just ran her over. She couldn't speak or cry. Curtis explained that she would be okay, and that whatever the doctor felt was best for Queene that's what she was going to go with. Curtis also mentioned that Queene had been battling this for a little over a year and that Chewy didn't know, but he would tell her when the time was right. He wanted Carla to talk to Queene soon. Carla was still in shock. She didn't say anything. She walked upstairs in her room and laid in her bed crying. She wanted to text James, but they haven't been on good terms but for some reason.

She wanted to text her first love Jayshawn and she did.

"Hey, I know we haven't spoken in a long time, but I wanted to check on you to see how you were doing?"

She also texted Remi and she knew Remi would call crying. Remi loved Queene and always told Carla to talk to her mother. She always told her that she only had one mother and that their relationship was important. She contemplated on what and how she was going to start the conversation because she didn't have that bond or relationship with Queene.

Around 9 o'clock that night, Queene arrived in the house with Chewy and she looked worn out. Carla had never seen her mother look like that. Carla wanted to take it easy. So, Carla started with a kind hello.

Queene was shocked to hear her speak

Hi Carla, how are you?

The question mom is how are you doing?

I could be better but I'm tired and just would like to rest. Are you okay Car?

Mommy we need to talk, and I want you to hear me out please. I have been battling with myself for some years now because I have been angry with you. I was so angry to the point where I missed out on the love you always had for me. No matter what you did, Chewy always loved you and I never understood why. Carla started crying. But mommy I love you and forgive you. Daddy told me you were sick, but before I found this out, I wanted to come to you, but I didn't know how.

Queene was a big ball of emotion she was sobbing and crying uncontrollably.

Carla, she said as she continued to cry, I never meant to hurt you or your sisters. I was a drug addict. I let the drugs take over terribly. I was wrong. I have been clean for some time now and I have moved on. Everyone accepted me back into their life but you. She cried even harder. Yes, I am sick, but I told your father I rather just die because I messed up with my daughters. I also told him that in order for me to get this surgery that I had to make it right with you because my girls are my life and if I don't make it, you would know I love you no matter what.

Carla interrupted her mother: Mommy I will be here for you! Because of my selfish ways I missed out on my mother and daughter bond.

Oh no you didn't it just began I am going to beat this cancer you hear me!

Queene walked up to Carla and gave her a big hug. Carla wrapped her arms around her mom and cried even more. Queene didn't want to let go, but she backed up and said to Carla "listen I didn't tell Chewy yet because she is a little younger, but I think it's time to tell her because I'm ready to kick this cancer ass and get it removed." Carla said mommy don't worry I will tell Chewy. Queene agreed and thanked Carla. As she went upstairs, she looked down the steps and said, "Carla I love you." Carla replied back with "Mommy I love you too!"

Chewy was in the living room watching YOUTUBE when Carla walked in. She had straightened herself up so that she could talk to Chewy. She had already knew Chewy was a very smart girl so she couldn't water anything down with her, so she sat next to Chewy.

"What do you want Carla? Move over! Give me some breathing space", Chewy said.

Carla slid over more to Chewy and hugged her.

CARLAAAA what? What is wrong with you?

Nothing, just checking on you and I wanted to spend some time with you that's all.

Okay that's fine. But really Carla what do you want I'm young but not stupid. Carla took a deep breath.

Okay Chewy you are very smart, and I have to tell you something but no matter what we will always have each other. Christina is away at college and she has her own life so we will always have each other.

Chewy looked up to Carla and said "C" your scaring me what's wrong?

Chewy mommy has cancer.

Huh what's cancer?

It's a disease that makes you sick and if you don't treat it you can die. You can also treat it and beat it, or it can always come back.

Chewy started to cry, well is mommy okay? She's not going to die, is she?

No Chewy she will be okay we are going to put it in God's hands. She wants us all to be there while she goes to surgery. Can you promise me that you will be strong? Also, that we won't let this break us, mommy will be fine. Chewy sobbed and sobbed and finally agreed that she would be there for Queene but also she made Carla promise that she would be there every step of the way, even though Carla felt some type of way about their mother. She agreed! Chewy still cried though because she was puzzled, she just didn't understand why? Minutes went by and Chewy still was deeply hurting so, Carla held her until she fell asleep. She knew that this would be a rollercoaster ride, but she knew that the backbone would be her and her father, so she had to stay strong and pray for better days.

Better Days

Chapter 8

Love

Love is a very intense word. The word stands for so much but yet gets tossed around for personal use. Love is beautiful. Love ISN'T supposed to hurt. If you ask me there are many levels to love. In this chapter it explains how I had to love myself with real events and scenarios that happened. So did the characters.

So much was going on with Queene that Carla had forgotten all about James and she really didn't care about anything but her mother and school. She thought about him but knew he had moved on and that was okay because she had put her life on hold. She often called Remi to talk to her, but Remi was busy with Da'Marie. She was dealing with

Da'Meire and that fact that he was about to go to college. Carla had planned a girl's night at her house just for just Remi the baby and Chewy. Carla wanted to be around true family and friends and Remi agreed she was so happy to spend time with them. Da'Marie was a few months and she was now in daycare because Remi had to go to school and pick up a part time job. Some days Dae's mother got the baby and so did Remi's mother when she didn't have work, so it all worked out.

Friday night came and Carla was excited. She went to Red Box with her dad's credit card and got a few movies. She ordered Chinese food, bought snacks, got a little bottle of Hennessey, and got her weed and blunts for the weekend. Remi got there about 8:45 and they didn't even greet her.

Everyone at the house took Da'Marie and kissed all over her. Chewy loved babies, she couldn't stop smiling. Da'Marie was a happy baby as long as she was fed, dry, and had some attention. She had a lot of it. Queenie carried Marie and baby talked with her until she passed out. Chewy started the movie and Carla whispered to Remi "let's go outside to get some air." Remi agreed! The baby was sleep and Queene watched her as she slept.

The girls went outside, and Carla cracked the blunt down and took a sip of Henny. She gave some to Remi. Carla started off with "Bitch I'm so glad you came over with the baby I miss you! I know you're a mother now and life is real, but to kick it with my bitch is clutch." Remi sipped slowly. "I know girl my life changed drastically, but I promised myself I would keep shit together.

 With Dae going off to college soon, and trying to get into this Performance Arts School, taking care of Da'Marie, high school, and work man I be so tired. Dae and I are on and off, we fuck here and there, but it definitely isn't how it used to be." "I be catching his dumb ass doing shit like flirting. His phone rings and he doesn't answer it. Just a lot of that weird dumb shit, but I can careless. I'm not saying he's not a good father to our baby, but it's not enough." "His life never stopped, and mines did, but I will never let Marie know that. I will make sure we're good. Nothing is promised you know?" She hit the blunt and faded. "So, I'm just living, feel me?" Carla was already in a daze because she had already hit the blunt a few times and drank half of her cup of Henny. "Man, I don't know where life is taking me, Carla began. My mom got the surgery and beat the cancer, but she still has her weak days. I basically been raising Chewy because my sister is in college and only came down the first day of my mom's surgery." "My dad is trying to work and be there for us. I'm ready to go to a trade school and get a job. Remi shit I don't know what's up with James and at this point I don't even care. I been thinking about Jayshawn for some reason." -- Remi interrupted Carla and said, "what bitch you lying!" "What!" Carla laughed, "Yes he is my first love. I know he may be in a new relationship, but shit I just want to see were he's at with life." Remi looked surprised but she knew that Jayshawn had been trying to reach out to Carla for a while now so for them to talk would be a good thing.

Carla enjoyed this time with Remi they were faded off Hennessey and weed cracking up about stories. They were talking and when Remi looked up it was 1:30 in the morning. Remi was shocked. She ran back in the house and there slept Chewy with baby Da'Marie in Queene's arms. Remi and Carla went back outside to laugh drink and smoke until they passed out. Remi knew Da'Marie really didn't sleep all night but Queene had put a spoonful of cereal in her milk, so she slept until 6:00am. Remi was on her baby girls schedule, so she woke up and headed into the house. Da'Marie was squirming and she started to fuss so Remi knew she was wet and hungry. Queene had felt Da'Marie and woke up.

Carla came in afterwards and laid on the couch next to Chewy and fell back to sleep. Remi was too busy nurturing her baby. Da'Marie was fed, dry, and she went back to sleep. Remi sat and watched her. She still couldn't believe that she had a baby and that she was a mother. She knew it was real, but she had so much going on with school, dance, and her job. She was determined to get in the dance school she always wanted. This was real life. In order to succeed Remi knew that she had to stick to her plan, so that she herself and her baby would have a better life and she planned too. Nothing or no one would interfere. She made daily weekly monthly and yearly goals. With prayer and strength, she had knew that it would be okay and "Better Days" would sure be coming.

It had been some time now and Remi and Carla were now

juniors. Da'Marie was 2 years old going on 3 and life just kept rolling. Queene had surgery a year back and she was now a cancer survivor. She also lost her left breast, but Queene was grateful she was able to see her kids grow up. Chewy was leaving 8th grade and looked very developed to be her age. Chewy was fast. She used her beauty and body to get what she wanted. One day she was out with her friends, and a guy that had dealt with her mother back in the day followed Chewy home. When she got a block away, he jumped out the car and asked her was she Queene's daughter? Chewy was scared but couldn't run. She answered "Yes." He grabbed her and threw her in the car. Chewy fought and fought and he beat her bad. He raped Chewy and beat her more until she passed out. Chewy was still alive to hear him say "your mom still owes me from years ago." "She smoked all the crack I gave her, and now you will pay." The guy had kicked Chewy out the car in a wooded ditch and the next day Chewy woke up in the hospital. She couldn't move. Her jaw was wired shut, both eyes were barely open, she had bruises all over her body, and whoever found her said she was naked. The doctor came in and talked to Queene, Carla, and Curtis. He informed them that Chewy was attacked and raped. She had been beat up very bad, she wasn't able to speak, and was very weak. Chewy knew what her attacker looked like but couldn't talk so she wrote everything down. Curtis had asked his daughter what happened. She wrote down:

MOMMY.

Curtis replied back: mommy what?

Chewy wrote very weak: Mommy's pimp he raped me and beat me.

Curtis lost it! Queene began to cry and wail, "That bitch less of a man raped my daughter and beat her! He must die" Queene cried out. Curtis was furious and spoke to Chewy again. "Baby listen to daddy please what color car was he driving?"

Chewy wrote: Black. Daddy he hurt me!

Curtis couldn't hold his composure. He was in a rage. All because of Queene, his daughter was hurting and in pain. He looked up at Queene and said, "You did this it's all your fault!" "You are the reason our daughter is laying in this bed now." Carla was so shocked to hear her dad talk to his wife like this. Queene shot back "I'm sorry I didn't know." Curtis stopped her.

"You didn't know what Queene huh?" He yelled louder. The doctor came in the room to control Queene and Curtis. The doctor knew how hurt Queene and Curtis were, but he instructed them to calm down and be there for Chewy. She suffered a concussion and head trauma as well. Once everything calmed down between them, the doctor wanted to continue running tests.

I will have my team come in to do a rape kit so that if he left any evidence this should help us. In the meantime, I want you to talk to Children's Youth and Families. Curtis yelled out "OH HELL NO!" "We are good parents why do we have to talk to them? They are not taking my kids away from me." The doctor continued, "We need you and your wife to participate. There will also be an investigator coming in to talk to you both. This is serious your daughter is very young, and we want to catch who did this to her." Before the Dr. exited the room, he told the two to pray and cooperate. Curtis was so angry that he couldn't even talk as Chewy laid there lifeless.

Carla called Remi and told her the devasting news and Remi came to support her friend. Dae had the baby and told her to go be by her side and Remi and her mother rushed to the hospital. Remi entered the room and instantly start crying. She had never seen a person so beat up. She cried and asked, "who had done this Chewy?" Carla said, "one of my mom's old pimps beat Chewy up!" Carla was angry and in a rage. She started to feel the hate coming back towards her mother all over again.

Days had gone by and they took turns sitting with Chewy's lifeless body. She slept all day and barely opened her eyes because they were swollen shut. She woke up from the touch of the sponge baths that Queene and Carla gave to her daily. Finally, after two weeks of Chewy being in the hospital the swelling of her eyes went down, but they were still black. Thankfully she was able to see. Chewy had done physical therapy two times a week to get her strength back. She still couldn't eat anything because her jaws were wired shut. Chewy had wires on her teeth but she was grateful that she was alive. Carla had got her a journal to write down her thoughts so that she wouldn't become depressed. Chewy wrote in her journal daily.

Day 20

I been sitting here in this hospital lifeless and angry. I got raped and beat half to death from a nigga that had it out for my mom years ago. I'm so angry please God take this pain away because I'm going to find out where he's located and shoot him dead. Well I got to go; I have to do physical therapy.

Ttyl

Chewy

Day 21

Fuck! I want to get out of this hospital. I can't eat, sleep, nothing. I heard the doctor talking and I should be home by early next week. I hope so. I just want to get better. I'm tired of people walking in checking on me and I want a long hot shower. Plus, I miss my friends and bed. A couple more days. Please this can't be life! Okay got to go I'm going to sleep.

Chewy

With everything that was going on with Chewy, it put a damper on Carla's family. Curtis and Queene had separated. Queene went to live with her sister. She came to the hospital on the days Curtis didn't. Curtis and Carla had got word that Chewy was coming home so they set her room up downstairs so she wouldn't have to go up and down the steps. She was far from recovery but was clear to go home. Life was crazy at Carla's house. Queene couldn't sit in the same room with Curtis without arguing. One day Queene was leaving after giving Chewy a shower, but it went longer than expected. Curtis arrived and told her to get out. Queene couldn't take it anymore. She yelled out and cried. She knew that she had to fix this. Curtis grabbed Queene and escorted her out the house. The site of Queene made him sick; he was so in love but hated her so bad.

Carla tried to stay out of her parent's separation she also had a lot on her mind. Jayshawn was so stuck on her brain that she texted the last number she had for him. To her surprise he answered back with:

Hey what's up C?

Carla couldn't move. She was in shock, so she waited a minute to text back. Her phone went off again.

Jayshawn- I'm sorry to hear about what happened to your sister are you okay?

Carla- Yes, I'm okay. She's okay we are taking it one day at a time. How are you?

Jayshawn-Me, I'm good getting ready to go to college. I have a couple schools to pick from. I miss you Carla I never meant to hurt you. I would never in life put my hands on you.

Carla- As crazy as this sounds, I forgive you too Jay that's why I texted you. We can remain friends if you like?

Jayshawn- Yes, I would love that. I love you Carla.

Carla looked at the phone and texted back: I love you too talk to you later.

This had made Carla's day. She called Remi. The phone rung and Remi said hello sounding wore out.

Carla-Hello what you doing?

Remi- Nothing just put Dae down for a nap and I'm next.

Carla-Oh okay well I won't hold you long.

Remi- What's up C?

Carla I just got done texting Jayshawn. We cleared the air and went back to being friends.

Remi- All shit old boo is back up and running huh? Too bad Da'Meire and I aren't seeing eye- to-eye.

Carla- Wait…damn what happened?

Remi- Nothing major. He has become the best father there is, but I been catching little fly shit like text and calls. We haven't been kicking it lately. NOTHING! When he comes to visit or get Da'Marie it's an in and out thing. I'm so focused though. I use the time that Marie is gone to sleep, catch up on shows, work, and go to dance practice I made a promise to myself and Da'Marie that I would finish high school and get into a dance school.

Carla- I feel you Remi you inspire me.

Remi- No I done had a baby my first year of high school and thought my life was over, but I won't quit. I'm far from inspirational though.

Carla- I love you girl, I'm trying to find myself. My family is all over the place after Chew's situation. She's finally home, but my mom and dad are damn near done. They can't even stand to stay in the same room as one another. My dad thinks it's Queene's fault for Chewy being beat and raped so my mom moved all her stuff out the house and went to go live with my aunt.

Remi- Dang C you going thru it. One thing I can say is your very strong and overcame so much. Do not let this get you down. Your mom is a good woman and she came a long way. That guy that did that to

Chewy been had a hidden agenda. Your mom has been clean for years now DON'T BLAME HER.

Carla-Huh don't blame…

Remi- Listen to me it's not about you and not about your mom. She lived a life she wasn't proud of unfortunately it caught up with her with the wrong person but she's sorry I know she is. Forgiveness is key Carla. Chewy is the victim she's going to need counseling and a strong support system. Now it's up to you to bring Queene and Curtis back together so that Chewy can heal.

Carla- I guess you're right I have to make it right. You always know what to say I love you with everything in me.

Remi- I love you too and I'm tired as hell so call me later. Bye C.

Carla- Bye Remi.

Carla had let her, and Remi conversations sink in and put a plan together and got on her hands and knees and prayed for better days.

Better Days

Chapter 9

Music

Growing up and still to this very day my love for music is at an all-time high. Music was the cure to everything in my life, when I didn't have anyone to talk to, I turned to music. This chapter was named music because Remi also loved music, she was put in a life that she didn't know how she could make better. Other than making it right and getting accepted in dance school.

Remi had given Carla so much good advice that she herself had to apply it to her life. She always wanted to dance on Broadway or in plays it didn't matter. She and Da'Meire had officially broke up and she was more focused. Although the two had broken up, Dae and his family did their part with the busy toddler. Dae was in college, but every chance he got he came to spend time with their daughter. Remi's mother, stepdad, and brothers were a big help as well. Music was Remi's life following dance. She felt so much better when she listened to certain music. Remi was so versatile. She listened to Patti Labelle, Luther Vandross, Brandi, Monica, Keyshia Cole, Biggie, Tupac Pink, Garth Brooks, Selena to Rae Schrumard, and twerking music. Whatever mood she was in she listened. Remi had put so many applications in for several dance schools. A couple were out of town as well. She wanted to achieve her goals and didn't want to let Da'Marie down. Trying to finish up high school was hard, but she had to. Things started to get harder. Remi's mom had gone back to work full time. Her brothers were still in school. Her stepdad got a new position at work, so they were busy. Da'Meire was playing college football and his mother tried to get Da'Marie when she could. Remi started to get stressed it got so bad that she had to take Da'Marie to auditions. Some recruiters turned her away. Remi had got her license and saved up and got her a little back and forth car to get her and Da'Marie around. Remi had received a letter in the mail from Ohio University and they offered her a scholarship and wanted her to come for an audition. Remi was excited but nervous at the same time. She would have to leave home and move to Ohio if she got accepted, but that's the risk she would have had to take. On that day in particular yet again she had no sitter and started to panic she just knew it was over. She also knew that this was an opportunity of a lifetime, so she prayed and had taken the risk of bringing Da'Marie.

She packed them clothes, snacks, food, water and blankets for the ride. Da'Marie was so happy she hollered ma, ma, ma, ride, ride. Remi smiled at her and said, "yes baby ride you have to be a big girl for mommy though okay Da'Marie?" Marie shook her head yes…Remi was ready she filled her gas tank up with 50 dollars and started their journey. She knew that she couldn't ride it out, so she had to stop to let Da'Marie out to feed her change her. She prayed the whole ride there that they didn't turn her away because she had her daughter in attendance. The ride went fast, and Remi started to panic, but she knew that Da'Marie didn't sleep the whole ride and was ready for a nap. As she pulled up to Ohio University, Da'Marie drifted off.

Remi still was a little scared to have to carry her daughter inside, get ready, and remain focused while still watching her daughter. The line was so long, and Remi went in to register. She had Da'Marie on her hip and first impressions are everything. The lady looked at her in shock. If looks can kill, Remi would be dead. Remi knew she had to do something and quick. She didn't want to feel like she rode up there for nothing. She had a chance to get accepted into a university to make things right for her and Da'Marie. She paced the floor and it seem like the time was going faster, Remi was only six people away then it was her turn to take the stage. She started to worry Da'Marie was still asleep in the big recliner that sat in the audition room. She stretched and got dressed to perform. All she could think about was smoking a fat blunt to ease her mind, but she had quit weeks ago. Remi looked around the room and earlier that day she had ran into a girl that had come in after her. She was so polite and gave Da'Marie compliments while she was sleep. They talked as if they had known each other for years. As bad as it looked to other people, Remi had a plan.

She was going to ask her new friend Lynn to keep an eye on Da'Marie as she was on stage auditioning. To her surprise she agreed and promised that she would be outside of the door cheering her on with her daughter in hand. Remi gave Lynn the biggest hug and they continued to practice on their routine. 15 minutes later it was Remi's turn. She went over to Da'Marie and held her tight and prayed with her.

God,

I come to you in the most thankful and humble way to keep me safe on the stage, to guide me through, and to keep Da'Marie safe back there with Lynn. Thank you for having her here today to watch over our angel. Hope that we both do well.

Amen

Remi was ready. She was anxious, excited, and scared. Her dance was called "Da'Marie" she explained to the judges why it was named after her daughter and as she was talking, she almost broke down crying because she ended her speech with "even if I don't make it. I tried for Da'Marie."

The music started and Remi went to work. She mixed jazz, hip hop, and a little soul in performance. She also reenacted certain parts of the song. She was quick and swift with her moves, splits, and back bends. Remi gave the judges handshakes during the performance; she was all around perfect. As she exhaled deeply to catch her breathe the, judges talked amongst each other and told Remi that she had done a wonderful job. She could use just a little more work but after the end of the conversation the lady said excitedly "WELCOME TO OHIO UNIVERSITY OF SCHOOL AND DANCE!" Remi cried on the stage. She was stuck. She couldn't move. She fell on the floor in tears that couldn't be held back. All of her hard work paid off. As she picked her head up and looked in the far back of the room, Lynn had Da'Marie in her arms as promised. Marie was so excited for her mom she yelled "Ma, Ma, Ma." Remi cried even harder. She couldn't believe that she got accepted in the 11th grade with a two-year-old daughter. She couldn't have been prouder of herself. She exited the stage were Lynn had tissues for her. Remi thanked Lynn so much and hugged her daughter tight. She looked at Marie and said, "I did it for you mamas." She then watched Lynn take the stage as promised. Lynn did a wonderful job as well.

She was more of a country pop music type of girl, but her audition was catchy, and the judges were impressed. Lynn wasn't too much into the judges like Remi was, but she gave them a show. She too had made it into the dancing school! Lynn had exited the stage jumping up and down breathing hard. She gave Remi a hug and they exchanged numbers and told each other they would see each other soon.

Remi had to call her mom and Carla with the good news. She was so pumped up. After minutes of talking to her mother, Remi had hung up to call Carla. Carla picked up the phone sounding sad, but Remi was so happy she wanted Carla to hear the good news. Remi interrupted Carla's hello and screamed "I did it I made it into Ohio University!"

Carla was still silent and then she said Congratulations to Remi. Carla was very dull and couldn't hold it in any longer she started to cry. Remi had gathered her belongings and made her way to her car. She strapped Marie in and put Carla on speaker. "C what's wrong?" Remi asked. Carla had told Remi that Queene only had six months or less to live and that the cancer had come back and spread. But that's when Queene talked to her doctor. That was six months ago when he had told her the bad news, but so much was going on with Chewy and her relationship with their father, she didn't tell anyone so now she's in the ICU fighting for her life. The doctor can't control the cancer and she had days to weeks left to live. Remi started to cry with Carla. This news was devastating to hear after getting good news. She had set that to the side for her friend.

Carla had asked the family and friends to come see Queene because her days were limited. Remi agreed as she drove back in total shock. She called her mom again, but this time to give her the bad news. Remi's mother had said a prayer for Queene and the family. She also prayed for safe traveling mercies to Remi and her granddaughter. Remi drove and only stopped once to get Da'Marie fed and changed, and she made it home quick. She had put Marie in the tub and put her to bed. She was very emotional. She didn't know what to think. Remi's mind was everywhere. Once Marie was sleep Remi had taken a nice long shower and after went into her mother and stepdads' room and talked to them. It was a bittersweet moment. She talked to them about the auditions and how she had to take Da'Marie with her. She didn't want to leave anything out. Remi's parents were proud of her and knew better days would come her way.

Chapter 10

MISUNDERSTOOD

Throughout my life I was and still feel like I'm very misunderstood. For me I come off as very outspoken and strong minded, and a weak mind would and does feel like I'm being offensive, and they misunderstand me. This chapter is about forgiveness because even with feeling misunderstood you have to FORGIVE. The characters want to be forgiven for their past and want to improve. I too have been working on my future s that my past won't hurt me.

Crazy thing about life is having no one to really relate to you, no one to talk to. Yes, there are million and one people to talk to, but to actually listen and understand what a person is going through is the key to understanding. Being misunderstood can really take a toll over your mind body and soul.

Queene had fought months, days, and minutes to her death. She was surrounded by her loved ones as she had taken her final breath. Curtis wanted Queene to be comfortable so he decided that she come home. Days before, Chewy had went into her room where she laid comfortably and talked to her mom. Queene didn't speak much, but she responded with a head nod. Chewy laid her head on her mother's bed and cried out. She said, "Mommy I know you never meant for us to have this life, and that you tried you're very best to clean yourself up, and I am very grateful that you did." Chewy cried harder. She continued. "Mommy I love you, and I know it wasn't your fault that I was raped and beat." When she looked at her mom, she seen tears flowing from Queene eyes. Queene tried to talk. She had taken her journal and attempted to write, but her hands were shaking very bad. She did make out that she loved her girls and that she was sorry! I'm so weak please forgive me she wrote. Chewy always forgave her mother. She was a mommy's girl, she laid by Queene's side and talked to her mom for hours until she heard her mother soft breath of her sleeping. She wanted her mom to get some rest, so she left the room to go talk to Carla. When she came onto the porch, she could smell the weed and Henny in the air. She sat next to Carla and began to talk.

Chewy- Hey C let me hit that blunt?

Carla- Here Chewy just hit it a couple times.

Chewy- Carla you know mommy is sick right? We need to make amends; we don't know how much longer she has.

Carla- Chewy come on you blowing my high I know mommy's sick that's why I'm here by her side.

Chewy- But no are you just here? Do you forgive mommy for everything she put us through? You're holding on to a grudge that Queene has NO CONTROL of. Mommy is sick and she needs us. That man took my innocence and my self-esteem for a while and nobody understood me, but as I got stronger and better, I accepted her apology. She didn't know that man was going to come years later. So, fuck all the hate you have for mommy let's make it work. I even seen dad in there talking to her.

Carla really couldn't forgive her mother and seeing her little sister beat up and raped she was full of anger. The next couple of days Queene had taken a turn for the worse. Curtis had called all of the family members. Queene was now on life support inside their home, and Carla still didn't know how to talk to her mom. Weeks before, Queene had wrote Carla a letter and gave it to Curtis just in case it was too late. She told him to give it to her if she passed away without talking to her. That's just what happened. Queene had passed away in her home around family and friends. Carla and Chewy's older sister Christina took it hard. She cried loudly only because she felt like she didn't do enough because she was away in college. Curtis also had taken Queene's death hard.

Although she was an addict, he loved her. He helped her get clean and paid for rehabs, there were times were Queene stole money off of Curtis and her kids to kick her habit and Curtis never gave up on her. He cried at her bedside and promised to take care of the girls. Queene laid there and looked peaceful. Even though she didn't get to talk to Carla, she had written that note. Carla walked up to the bed and kissed her mother's forehead and told her mother sorry. She sobbed softly because it was over, and her mom was gone. She was so angry at her mother that she didn't get a chance to talk. Although Chewy was the youngest, she didn't shed a tear because she had talked to her and accepted her apology. She was a mommy's girl and really in shock.

When the funeral home came to pick up Queens Body, that's when Chewy took it the hardest she screamed out "it's NOT FAIR MOMMY PLEASE COME BACK I NEED YOU!" "MOMMY, MOMMY she cried more." The funeral director instructed Curtis to try to calm Chewy down so that they could do their job. Chewy yelled out louder "MOMMY PLEASE DON'T LEAVE ME PLEASE." Chewy was hurting. She cried uncontrollably to the point where Curtis had to walk her upstairs. He knew that once they zipped the bag up with Queene's body inside Chewy was going to lose it. As the night ended Chewy cried. She had never been so hurt before in her life she felt like she kept getting robbed out of life. She had so many thoughts running through her head that made her cry more and more. She didn't want to be here anymore. Chewy knew that her dad owned a loaded gun in his closet for the safety of the house. She contemplated going back and forth. Chewy was lifeless. In a small timeframe, she had been beaten and raped, and then her mother died and left her. She died right in front of her; what was there to live for? Her oldest sister never was around, and Carla couldn't even make amends with her mother before she passed away. LIFE JUST ISNT FAIR. Chewy felt MISUNDERSTOOD! She didn't want to be alive ANYMORE! She went into her father's closet and grabbed the gun and locked herself into the bathroom. She was shaking so bad. Chewy cried and put the gun to her head and then heard a loud knock at the door. Chewy's dad bust down the door because he had heard Chewy crying. He also went into his room and seen that the gun was out of the box that it was in.

After busting down the door he ran into the bathroom and had taken the gun off of Chewy. She cried in his arms and said, "Daddy I want to die please let me go," "Mommy's gone I don't want to be here." Curtis yelled for Carla and Christina to come in the bathroom. As they ran, upstairs they heard Chewy and Curtis crying. They sat in the bathroom Curtis talked to all three of his daughters and told them that "They have to stick together." He explained that Chewy is taking it very hard and that she tried to take her life. He told them there is no time to be weak. "Your mom loved every last one of you" Curtis pulled out an envelope and gave it to Carla." "Read this. Your mother knew that you weren't going to be able to talk to her before she passed away." Carla cried because she knew that her mom loved her, but because of her selfish ways it was all over and all she had was this letter.

Curtis had got Chewy together and laid her in bed to sleep. Queene's oldest daughter Christina made the funeral arrangements for their mother. Carla went inside her room to read the letter that Queene had written, but first she looked down at her cell phone and she had 16 missed calls. Some from Remi and her mother, but they had already been here when her mother passed away and three from Jayshawn. He also texted her and gave his condolences and wanted to be by her side. She read the text and put everything on hold until she read her mom's letter. Carla was shaken up with all that was going on but opened the letter and read it. The letter started off,

Carla,

I just want to say if you're reading this letter I am officially gone, and we didn't get a chance to talk. Baby I love you so much and I'm glad we were able to talk when we did. I also know that you are still angry with me because of what happened to Chewy, but I never meant for that to happen. I was never perfect, and I cleaned my life up for you and your sisters, but most importantly for myself. I want you to let all the anger and hurt go. I am gone now. Please take care of Chewy and watch over your father. Don't mourn me. Make me proud and remember let it go Carla. I love you always and forever.

Queene

Carla was full of tears that she couldn't hold in. She got on her hands and knees and asked God for forgiveness and she asked that if her mother had reached heaven that she wanted to tell her sorry. After the funeral, days and months went pass, and Curtis wanted to move into another house. The house they lived in had so many memories of Queene. Queene's eldest went back to college and months later got married, so Carla, Chewy, and Curtis moved an hour away from their home where all of their memories were.

Remi called Carla up and told her that when she got accepted to the college she couldn't stay home because it was too far to drive every day. She wouldn't take no for an answer and she wanted Carla to move with her and Da'Marie in a three-bedroom house ten minutes away from the dance studio in Ohio. Carla hesitated for a while because it was still fresh of her mother's passing and she wanted to take care of Chewy, so she told Remi she would get back to her. Remi and Carla were in their last year of high school and even with all of what was going on, Carla managed to walk across the stage and receive a diploma with her mother's ashes in a locket around her neck. She and Remi had done it. Da'Marie screamed in the crowd "mommy, mommy!" Everyone was so proud that throughout all of the pain and setbacks they went through, it was all over and they were ready to move on.

After graduation Remi had asked Carla what her answer would be because she was leaving next week. Carla still hadn't talked to her dad or Chewy but told Remi she would talk to them while everybody was all together, and that's just what she did. Carla had sat them down and started the conversation:

Now that I graduated, I must move on. Remi wanted to know if I would like to come move with her and Da'Marie.

Curtis- Huh? Carla that's far baby!

Chewy- Sis go head do your thing.

Carla smiled at Chewy and said-

Chewy I will, and when I get myself together, I'll come back for you. I always wanted to go to school for social work and they have a drug and alcohol rehab up there where I can apply once I'm hired, I would like to sit and tell mommy's story. I'm going to keep Queene name alive. Now that she's gone, it made me realize a lot. You only get one mom and when she left a little piece of me left as well. I plan to live, and I want you 2 to live as well. Chewy, I want you to keep your head in those books and not these boys. They're going be here. Okay?

Chewy-Okay

She continued- And daddy go back to work and get your social life back. That's what mommy Queene would want. Don't forget her, but you have to live. You'll always have us. Christina is living her life with her husband, and we all love you and I promise to always be there for you. Once I'm on my feet I will come for Chewy I promise, Curtis cried but he finally agreed.

He ended the conversation- Carla you can always come back home. I know you leaving but stay out of trouble please. I want you home for Thanksgiving and Christmas at least. Okay?

Carla said- Daddy I promise I'll be back.

Curtis was really happy and said- Well before you go packing, your mother also had left us $30,000! She wanted us to split it four ways. We will get $7,500 each. Please use this wisely. Buy you a little car. Give Remi rent money until you can put a down payment on your own apartment. I will put it in your account so you can have it before you leave.

Carla was shocked and looked up and said mommy thank you. Chewy was also shocked but knew her father would help her manage her money. Curtis also called Christina and let her know as well. After the conversation ended Carla called Remi and happily told her the good news. Remi was so happy she couldn't help but to scream thru the phone. Remi and Dae didn't work out so she moved on and focused on her and her daughter because Dae was on the road a lot. He never had time anymore, so he sent money. Remi had taken that money and the money from her working and put a down payment on a three-bedroom two-bathroom rent-to-own condo. The days were going fast and before you knew it, Carla, Remi, and Da'Marie were on the road and ready to start their journey. All for better days.

Better Days

Chapter 11

AA'LAYAH (Beautiful Kind and Amazing) The ending of a painful experience. Bringing a new life to yourself is always good. Aa'Layah is my 3rd daughter and she has blessed me in so many ways. Maturity was one of the many things I had to learn and so did the characters in this chapter.

Remi started school and graduated in two years with a loan to open up her own dance studio. Da'Marie also graduated from kindergarten. Carla was still in school to become a social worker and worked part time at a rehab where she talks about her mother's addiction and how it affected her family. Carla also talked to Jayshawn from time to time and they began to plan to buy their first house soon.

Chewy was finishing up her 11th grade year in high school. She took a turn for the worst when she came across the guy who beat and raped her. She tried to kill him and was arrested. She eventually got off because they had taken his DNA and convicted him of rape and assault. Every summer Chewy visits Carla and Remi and plans on moving with Carla when she gets her own place.

There are things in life that will knock you down. It's your call as to if you're going to get back up and how it will affect you. There are so many scenarios in my book that people are going through or have went through. You have to keep God first and ask him to guide you from A to Z. NEVER GIVE UP because even when things get rough there will be, BETTER DAYS!

Love: Nina

Better Days

Chapter 12

My Journey (The End) it's never the end it's the beginning of you trying to get you back on the right track. I say this too myself all time to never rush on what you want to accomplish, because you see others succeeding. It may not be your season, and if that's the case be happy for the ones that are winning. Your time will come to enjoy your blessings, and with the process of waiting put the footwork in. Work hard and never give up!!! Your journey is not OVER keep going.

Trust me this is not the end for me, just the beginning. I felt all types of emotion off of this book. I really wanted people to know the real me and to really read and understand that you're not alone in any situation. My journey has made me mature to life. My eyes are open to a lot of things. Don't get me wrong, I'm still in a struggle and I go through everyday life situations. I just know how to cope and live. Life is all about how you make it. I know that people live for the future and yes that's a good way of living. I just try living day by day because nothings promised. The definition of journey is an act of traveling from one place to another. I traveled from so many things in my life good and bad. My journey was rough, but I made it through. To dance in the rain, you must first learn to praise him in the storm. I danced in the rain plenty of times in my journey.

But being a solider at war, I always kept God first through it all. Even still to this day. That's very important! Keep your head high and try not to sink. Don't suffocate your life because you only have one life to live. Always aim for "BETTER DAYS".

Made in the USA
Middletown, DE
19 March 2022

62797799R00099